Mindbending

Brain

Trickery

Managing Editor: Simon Melhuish
Series Editor: Nikole G. Bamford
Page layout and cover design: Al Shiner

Published by:
LAGOON BOOKS
UK: PO BOX 311, KT2 5QW, UK
US: 10685-B HAZELHURST DR. #9988, HOUSTON, TX 77043, USA

www.thelagoongroup.com

ISBN 978-1-907780-00-4

Batch Code: 09 15
Printed in China.

Mindbending
Brain
Trickery

Other titles in the Mindbending range include:

Mindbending Classic Logic Puzzles

Mindbending Conundrums & Puzzles

Mindbending Lateral Thinking & Puzzles

Mindbending Speed Puzzles

Mindbending Optical Illusions

INTRODUCTION

This book contains an amazing range of tricks –
tricks to fool your brain and fool your friends.

Your mind will be mystified by the classic illusions,
where colors and shapes play havoc with your
senses. Or you can bamboozle your friends and
family with astonishing feats of tomfoolery.

It's a sure-fire way to amuse everyone for hours.

Tell someone to think of the following:

What color is snow?
What color was Christian IV's white horse?
What does vanilla ice cream look like?

Now – imagine in your mind:
First, a polar bear blinking in a snowstorm.

Good, now imagine a blank sheet of paper and you with a pen in
hand sitting staring at it.

Good. Now quickly, on that blank piece of paper in your mind, write down
what cows drink. What did you write?

(And obviously, everyone says 'milk'.)

Another fun one is to ask people:

What's 20 + 25?
What's 15 + 12?
What's 12 x 9?

All right – now tell them to think of a color and a tool.

99% of people say
red hammer

Write it somewhere beforehand to
make them believe you're psychic.

Get a friend to pick any
two-digit number e.g. 49

x 3
x 7
x 13
x 37

**The final answer will be
the original number
written out three times!**

So 49 x 3 x 7 x 13 x 37
= 494949

Get a friend to pick any
two-digit number
e.g. 74

x 3367

To work out the final answer you have to imagine
the original number written out three times e.g. 747474
then divide it by three: 249158

This one takes practice, but it's very hard to see how it's done!

This is a good trick to play on a friend.

1. Pick a number between 1 and 10.
Multiply it by 9.

If it's a two-digit number, add them together.
Now subtract 5.

Right, now map the result to a letter of the alphabet,
where A = 1, B = 2 and so on.

Think of a country which begins with that letter.

Take the second letter of the country and think of an animal
which begins with that letter.

Think of the color of that animal…

You're thinking of a
gray elephant from Denmark, right?

Pick a three-digit number where the first digit is larger than the third digit by 2 or more.

Reverse that number by reading it backwards.

Subtract the smaller of these two numbers from the larger one.

Add the result to its own reverse.

e.g. 321 − 123 = 198
198 + 981 = 1089

Why is this always equal to 1089?

Place these fourteen dots along the sides of a square in such a way that there are an equal number of dots along each side.
Solution on page 94.

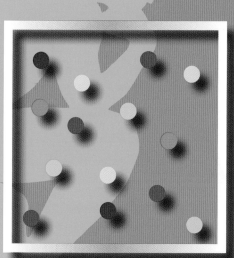

One barrel has oranges (O), one has lemons (L) and one has a mix of both oranges and lemons (M). All three have been incorrectly labeled. How can you tell which is which if you are only allowed to pick one piece of fruit from just one barrel? Solution on page 94.

Lay out 20 counters on a table.

Invite your opponent to go first and to pick up one, two
or three counters at once. Then you do the same.
The player who picks up the last counter wins.
The trick is to make two plays always add up to four.
So if your opponent picks up one counter, you pick up three,
two counters, you pick up two and three you pick up one.
You will always win if your opponent goes first.

Get three identical coins.

Warm two (on a radiator) and put one in the fridge.
Ask someone to lie on their back and put the cold coin on their
forehead. Then take it off and put the two warm coins on top of each
other on their forehead and ask them which they thought was heavier.

They will think they're equal even though there were two of
the warm ones.

Tell someone to write down a three-digit number (example: 746).
Tell them that you are each going to write down
another two three-digit numbers and add them.
But before you do, you are going to write down the sum total
of all these on a piece of paper and fold it up.

You obtain the answer by subtracting 2 from the last digit
of the first number and placing a 2 before the first digit.
Thus 746 becomes 2744 for the answer.

Now ask the other person to put their two digits down,
either both at once or in succession with you.
Either way, they must precede you.

Now whatever they put down, make each number,
when added to the number you put down, add up to 999.
Don't do this more than once with each person; they'll catch on otherwise.

Demo: (original number) 746 (their first number)
325 (your first number)
674 (their second number)
841 (your second number) 158
Total 2744

They unfold the paper and you're a hero!

Turning over two coins at a time, can you make three coins appear tails up in exactly three moves? Solution on page 94.

Which one of the cubes shown below cannot
be made from this flat one? Solution on page 94.

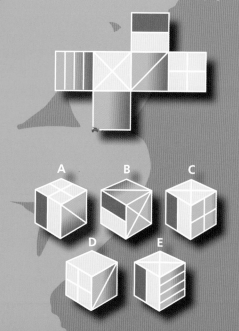

A

B

C

D

E

Tell someone to do the following:

(1) Write down a three-digit number (where the digits are different), and keep it hidden from you.

(2) Reverse the digits and write that number down.

(3) Subtract the smaller number from the larger number.

(4) Find the same page in the phone book as the answer in (3) and remember the first and last names of whoever is listed at the top of the first column there.

(5) Close the phone book.

(6) Tell you just the first letter of the last name.

You then open the phone book to the page containing that name and announce the full name of the person.

Here's how it's done:

Whatever number the person selects in (1), the answer in (3) will contain a 9 in the middle and the first and third numbers will add up to 9. If, for example, the person writes down 623, this number reversed will be 326. When 326 is subtracted from 623, the result is 297. Note that the middle digit of this answer is 9 and that the sum of the first and last digits is 9.

Whatever letter the person gives you as the beginning of the last name, there will only be one page number in the book (unless you live in an extremely populous city!) where the names begin with that letter, have a 9 in the middle and the first and third digits add up to 9. Find that page and read off the first name on it to the amazement of your victim.

Which pattern is the odd one out? Solution on page 94.

A

B

C

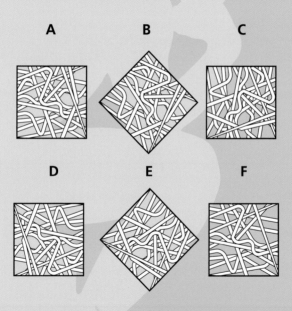

D

E

F

Can this map be colored with just three different colors,
e.g. red, yellow and blue, so that no two countries
touching each other are the same color? Solution on page 94.

Pick sixteen cards from a pack: the four kings, four queens, four aces, and four jacks. Now arrange them in a 4x4 square so that there is no card of the same suit next to each other along each row, column, or main diagonal. Solution on page 94.

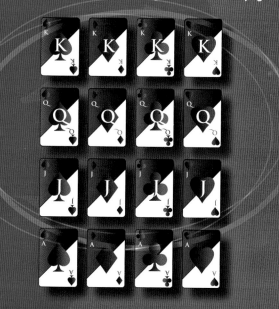

Ask a person or many people to choose any number, but to keep it a secret.

Tell them to do the following:

add 37 to the number, subtract 86, then add 3.

Now subtract the result from the original secret number.

No matter what the secret number is, everyone finishes with the same number – in this example, 46.

As an extra trick, write 46 on a paper in a sealed envelope and reveal at the end.

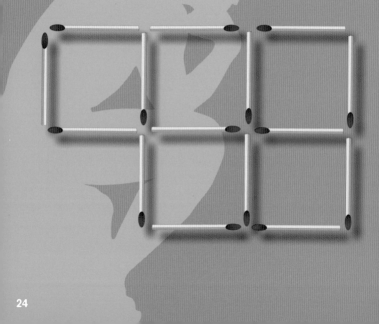

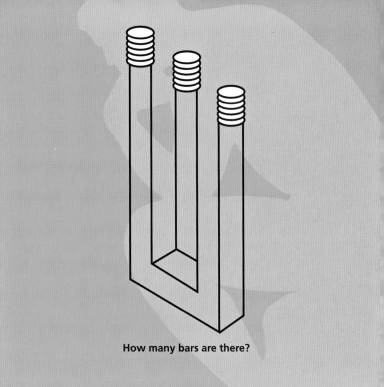

How many bars are there?

When the flattened die is folded, it will look like one of the other five dice below. Which one? Solution on page 94.

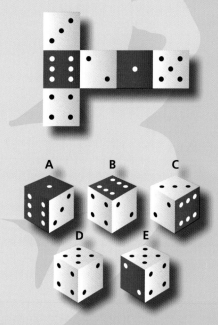

Ask people to pick a number between one and four –
about 49% will choose three and 49% choose two
(and 2% that choose one, or four, or 2.5 or any others).

However, if you phrase the question

"Pick a number from one to four"

then about 98% will choose three.

What's the reason?
In asking the question you vocalise the numbers 1, 2 and 4
(one to four). The brain immediately goes for the
'missing' selection – three.
You can go on from there to use this 'randomly selected'
three in any way you choose.

This is a tangram. Thousands of shapes can be made from just these seven. Cut the pieces of the tangram out of card and experiment.

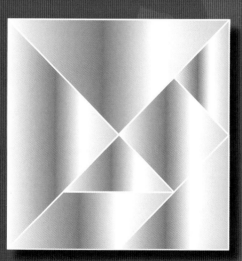

These four shapes are examples of what can be created.
How are they made?

This is a gag which you can use to get a laugh.

Hand a spectator a slip of paper and tell him to go to
the other side of the room and write a short sentence on the paper,
fold it and hand it to another spectator.

Appear to concentrate very deeply, and say,
"I will write the same as you on my slip,"
which you do.

Hand your slip to the spectator who is holding the other slip.
Ask him to open the spectator's slip and read it aloud.

Now you say,
"That's right. I wrote the same as you."
And that's exactly what you have written – just the four words,
'The same as you!'

You may vary this by writing,
'That's right' on a slip. Proceed as above.
Have the spectator's slip read aloud and then ask him to read your slip.
Of course, he will say, "That's right."

Here's a trick you can use to fool and amuse yourself,
as well as others.

Think of a small number.
Now double it, add 4, divide by 2.
Subtract the number you first thought of.
Your answer is 2. Right?

This works automatically.
For instance, say your first number was 3.
Doubled, it becomes 6, add 4 and you get 10.
Divide by 2, equals 5; subtract the number you first thought of (3)
and your answer will be 2.

When you do this, the answer will always be one half of the
number you add. When you repeat this, change the number
you tell people to add so that the answer will be different.
Remember, if you tell them to add 10, their answer will
be 5 – always one half of the number they add. Try it!

Move the coin and just three matches and make the fish swim in the other direction. Solution on page 94.

Do the horizontal lines look curved?
Get out your ruler and check.

Arrange five cards so that each card touches the
other four . Solution on page 94.

Which of the two men is larger? Solution on page 94.

Which of these two envelopes can you draw without lifting pen from paper, and without going over any line a second time? Solution on page 94.

Ask someone to pick a number in their mind from 0 to 9.
(Let's say 2). Tell them to double the number. (2 + 2 = 4).

Tell them to add five to the new number. (4 + 5 = 9).

Tell them to multiply the answer by five. (9 x 5 = 45).

Now tell them to remember the answer. (45).

Ask them to pick another number from 0 to 9. (In this case 4)

Ask them to add this number to their answer. (45 + 4 = 49).

Ask them to tell you the answer. (49).

Listen to it carefully and then in your mind subtract 25 from the total.
(49 – 25 = 24)

The first digit of the answer YOU get in
your mind after subtracting 25 (24)
is the first number they picked (2)
and the second digit is the second
number they picked (4).

Arrange these twelve straws to make six equally-sized segments. Solution on page 95.

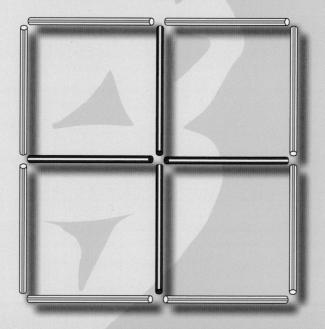

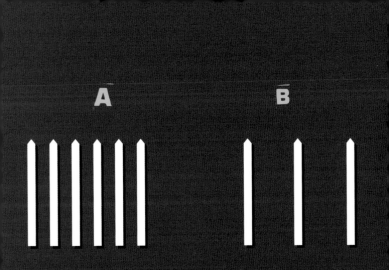

Which of the fences is wider? Solution on page 95.

How many triangles can you count in this picture? Solution on page 95.

When everyone is ready, start giving easy arithmetic questions rapidly.
For example: 2 + 2, 10 – 5, 6 x 2, etc.

Explain that people shouldn't worry about missing one or
getting them right… just write down the answers as fast as they can.

Shout out about 10 of these sums, then say:

"Write down the name of a vegetable!"

90% WRITE CARROT.

Think of a whole number
(an integer) bigger than zero

e.g. 4

Square it (multiply it by itself)

16

Add the original number

20

Divide by the original number

5

Add 17

22

Take away the original number

18

Divide by six

3

The answer is always three.

How many rectangles are there on a chessboard?
Solution on page 95.

Think of a whole number bigger than zero

e.g. 2

Multiply it by two

4

Add 10

14

Divide by two

7

Take away the original number

5

The answer is always five.

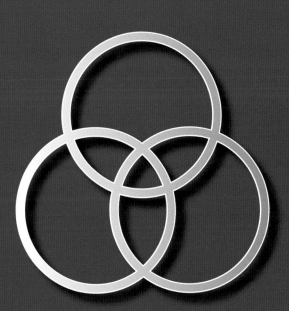

Can you draw the design above without lifting pen from paper or retracing your steps? Solution on page 95.

Which of these pieces will complete
the jigsaw opposite? Solution on page 95.

A

B

C

D

E

Can you decipher the following cryptic message? Solution on page 95.

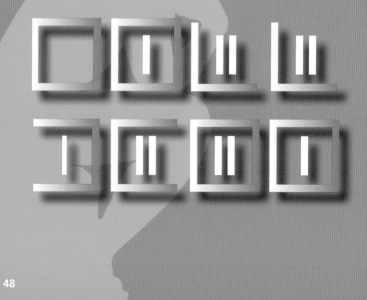

48

Pick a number from one to nine
[e.g. 8]

Double it [16]

Add five [21]

Multiply by five [105]

Pick another number from one to nine and add it
[e.g. 2 = 107]

To guess the two numbers, subtract 25 from the total [82]

The first digit is the first number and the second digit is the second number.

How can you make this equation correct by moving just one toothpick? Solution on page 95.

Which of the snooker cues is longer?
Solution on page 95.

If these views show a bird's-eye view and a head-on view
of an object, what is the side-view like? Solution on page 95.

BIRD'S-EYE

HEAD-ON

Pick a three-digit number
[e.g. 123]
Multiply by seven [861]
Multiply by 11 [9471]
Multiply by 13 [123123]

The answer will be

the original number twice.

Guess the Date

Pick a date [e.g. 1 January 2009]
Add 18 to the chosen month [19]
Multiply by 25 [475]
Subtract 333 [142]
Multiply by eight [1136]
Subtract 554 [582]
Divide by two [291]
Add the chosen day [292]
Multiply by five [1460]
Add 692 [2152]
Multiply by 20 [43040]
Add the last two digits of the chosen year [43049]
Subtract 32940 [10109]

The answer is the date in month/day/year format.

Can you draw the arrow and target above without taking pen from paper or retracing steps? Solution on page 95.

Divide the shape into four parts of equal shape and size. Solution on page 96.

The bolt on the right above would be screwing into a nut,
the bolt on the left would be unscrewing.

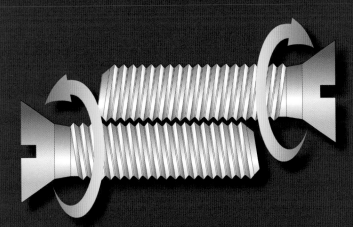

If these two bolts are touching, do these movements bring them
closer together or further apart? Solution on page 96.

Beginning with the letter 'E' at the top of the triangle, and reading down, always passing from a letter to an adjoining letter, how many ways is it possible to read 'equilateral'?

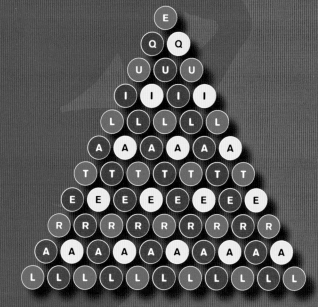

Pick a seven-digit number [e.g. 1234567]

Multiply the first three digits by 80 [9840]

Add one [9841]

Multiply by 250 [2460250]

Add the last four digits of the chosen number [2464817]

Add the last four digits of the chosen number again [2469384]

Subtract 250 [2469134]

Divide by two [1234567]

The answer is the original number

Can you find the four-leafed clover? Solution on page 96.

When in the Course of human events, it becomes necessary for one

people to dissolve the political bands which have connected

them with another, and to assume, among the powers of the earth,

the separate and equal station to which the Laws of Nature and of

Nature's God entitle them, a decent respect to the opinions of

mankind requires that they should declare the causes which impel

them to the separation.

Pick any word in the first (red) section of the text.
Then, skip as many words as there are letters in your chosen word.
For example, if you picked the fourth word ('Course') you have to
skip 6 words ('of human events, it becomes necessary') to end up on
the word 'for'... Repeat the process by skipping as many words as
there are letters in the successive words you land on.
What's the first word you encounter in the last (green) section?
Answer: God. Always.
(The sequence would continue with the words:
descent, that, causes.)

Here is a trick to play on your own brain.

Hold your arms out in front of you
and cross them over.
Rotate your hands so your palms face
each other then mesh your fingers together.

Now slowly rotate your hands up between your arms
so you're staring at your knuckles.
Ask someone to point to one of your
index fingers then attempt to move it.

You'll move the wrong one.

And another one to fool the gray matter.

Stand with your right side next to a wall,
then press your downwards-extended right arm against the wall,
pushing the balled back of your hand against the wall as
hard as you can, as if trying to push the wall away.

After about a minute of intense effort,
walk sideways away from the wall, relax, and laugh as your
right arm magically lifts on its own until it is at least
shoulder high, or sometimes, depending on the effort you
had expended, over your head.

If you faced the wall instead of standing rightside to it
while pushing with your right knuckles, stepping away,
you'd give an involuntary salute.

Tell someone you're going to brainwash them.

Ask them to say something, and once they finish saying it,
ask them a simple question, the answer to which they know,
but they're going to give you the wrong answer.

The typical response you'll get at this point is skepticism
(You're going to try to trick me? Okay, give it your best shot),
which makes the end result much sweeter.

Tell him or her to say the word 'ten' out loud ten times fast.
Tententententententententen.
Then ask them, "What is an aluminum can made out of?"
Their answer will be, "Tin."
Ask them again. "Tin!"

(They think they've eluded your trick, because they think you made them say
'ten' so that they'd say 'ten' instead of 'tin'.
They don't understand the ten times repetition of 'ten' was a distraction
so that they wouldn't comprehend the significance of 'aluminum can',

You'll usually be able to ask them the same question about a half dozen times,
getting the same wrong answer of 'Tin'.

Often, you can even slow your question down, even emphasize the word
'aluminum', and they'll still give you the same wrong answer.
After you've befuddled them with the ten trick, you can do it all over again by
doing the same trick, only this time substituting "step" for "ten",
which they must say ten times fast, then asking them,

"What do you do when you come to a green light?"
They'll answer, "Stop."

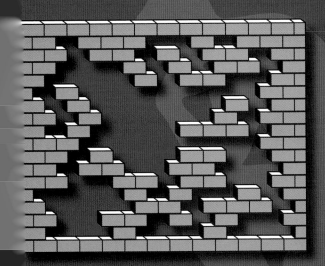

many bricks are missing from the wall? Solution on page 96.

Another mind game is to fold lengthways a piece of paper about four inches/10 cm high and eight inches/20 cm long, so you have a long tent shape two inches/5 cm high and eight inches/20 cm long.

On one of its sides, divide the side into four equal squares with vertical lines. In the first square write 1, in the second 2, in the third 3, in the fourth, 4. Keep this hidden.

While the person you want to play the game with is watching, cup your hand around a piece of paper, write on it, 'You chose 3', then fold the paper in half so it can't be read, or seal it in an envelope for a dramatic effect, and pass it over to them, telling them not to look at it yet.

Take out the long tent with the four numbers, not showing the numbered side to them yet. Ask them to quickly choose a number, then place the tent, numbered side to them, on the tabletop.

They'll almost always choose 3,

because of the way our minds work, we look first to the right of center.

Once they choose 3, tell them to unfold the paper you handed them, or open the envelope. They'll usually keep flipping the piece of paper with 'You chose 3' on it over and over, trying to figure out how you knew what number they would choose.

Ask a friend to write down ANY
three-digit number such as
231 or 884.
Ask them to multiply the number

x 7
x 11
x 13

...but even if your friend has used
a calculator, you will have written
down the answer ages ago!
It's fiendish!

THE SECRET:
all you do is write out the starting number twice!
So 231 will become 231231 and 884 will become
884884.

Ask a person to write down the year of his birth and then the year of his marriage, or his first year of school.

Then he must write down his age at the end of the present year and the number of years he has been married or the number of years since he began school.

In the meantime, you have written a total on a piece of paper and put it in an envelope.

The total of the person's figures will be the same as the total you wrote.

Here is the reason: the sum will always be twice the number of the present year.

Thus, if the trick is done in 1928:

Year of birth	1900
Year of marriage	1925
Age	28
Years since marriage	3
Total	3856

The number 3856 is two times 1928.

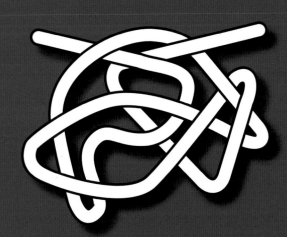

If you pulled on both ends of the rope,
would the rope knot? Solution on page 96.

Take any five-digit number
e.g. 76543
times it by 11
then multiply the answer by 9091

The final answer will be the original number twice!

So 76543 x 11 x 9091 = 7654376543

Divide this cake between four children so that each child gets a piece with two red sweets, which is exactly the same size and exactly the same shape as the pieces given to the other three children. Solution on page 96.

Lie down on the floor and close your eyes.
Get a friend to lift your legs up and hold them there for about two minutes.

Relax and think pleasant thoughts.

Then your friend needs to lower your feet very slowly.
Sounds boring but after a few seconds it'll feel like your legs are going through the floor.

Instead, they're still being lowered.

You'll need a friend for this trick as well.

Lie on your stomach with your arms stretched out above your head and your eyes closed.

Have a friend hold them as high off the floor as possible –
but not so it hurts. After about a minute,
your friend needs to lower your arms very slowly.
Like the previous experiment, you'll think your arms
should've touched the floor.

It feels like you're falling even though you're lying down.

Cross your middle finger over your index finger.
Now, slowly run the small 'gap' between your crossed
fingers along the ridge and around the tip of your nose.

You should feel two 'phantom'
noses under the tips
of your index and middle fingers.

Apparently, your motor-brain is tricked into thinking
that each finger is touching a separate nose!

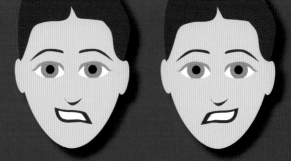

Which face is happier?

The only difference: the mouths, which are asymmetrical.
The left face is regarded as happier by the vast majority of
right-handers (and most left-handers).
Human faces are identified by the brain's right hemisphere,
so the mouth's left corner is the focus.

Look at the structure below. It's called a hypercard.
Two different views are presented.
Do you think it's possible to create such a structure out of
cardboard or paper, simply by cutting with scissors – not by using
glue or paste? Try doing it.

It may seem impossible, but look at the facing page...

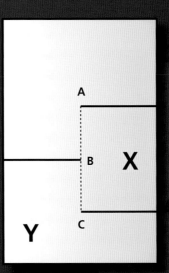

It is possible. Take a rectangular sheet of paper or cardboard and make three cuts along the black lines shown to the right. Now fold flap X up 90 degrees along the broken line ABC and then turn the lower portion Y over by folding it back 180 degrees along the broken line BC.

Voilà – a hypercard to put on your desk.

Sit down and lift your right foot,
moving it in clockwise circles.
Simultaneously, lift your right hand and
draw the number

6

in the air.

Your foot will change direction,
and you won't be able to control it.

Can you cut the sphinx into four pieces of exactly the same shape and size? Solution on page 95.

Flip through a deck of cards facing a friend so that both of you can see the faces on the cards rapidly shuffled. Tell her to glimpse at one of the cards being shuffled and to remember it.

In secret, slow down the flipping process imperceptibly at one card, and then continue through the shuffle.

The hesitation should be brief and unconscious to the spectator, but not to you. The spectator should mentally select that card, without knowing why.

After the cards are flipped through, pretend to 'guess' what it is!

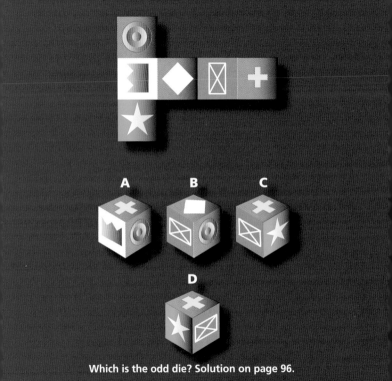

Which is the odd die? Solution on page 96.

Take a piece of paper with the words 'CARBON DIOXIDE' on it and hold it up at right angles to a mirror. The word 'CARBON' is reversed, what happens to the word 'DIOXIDE'? Solution on page 96.

CARBON

DIOXIDE

This requires two chairs and a blindfold.
The person wearing the blindfold should sit in the rear chair,
face towards the back of the person sitting in the front chair.
The blindfolded person should then reach around and place his hand on
the nose of the other person. At the same time he should place
his other hand on his own nose and begin gently stroking both noses.

After about 1 minute, more than 50% of the subjects
report their nose as incredibly long.
This is called Pinocchio's Effect.

This trick will confuse your photoreceptors.

This will temporarily blind you in one eye (for around 30 seconds but don't worry – it doesn't cause any harm)

Go into a room, shut the door and turn out the lights so that the room is mostly dark. Wait until your eyes adapt to the darkness. You should be able to make out the basic shapes of the room from the tiny bit of light coming in from under the door.

Next, close your right eye and cover it with your hand. Turn the light on, keeping your eye closed and covered.

Leave the light on for about a minute or until your left eye has adapted to the light. Uncover your eye and look around the darkened room. What do you see? What you might experience is an illusion discovered by researcher Uta Wolfe in which it seems that your left eye is closed, even though it is open.

The explanation for this is that the visual cycle takes time to adapt. When it is not adapted as for the left eye, the eye will send wrong signals to the brain, thus images would be darker for the left eye until it rectifies itself.

You have 10 glasses in a row and the first five contain liquid, the next five are empty. Can you alternate full and empty glasses by moving just two glasses? Solution on page 95.

Give two pieces of paper to someone,

one piece saying 1, the other 5.

Tell him that you'll guess which one he's holding in which hand. Turn your back and tell him to hold one paper in each hand.

Say that you want him to focus on the numbers and mathematics is the best way to get his mind in gear.

Ask him to multiply the number in the right hand by 2 and to say 'OK' when he has the answer.

Ask him to multiply the number in the left hand by 17 and to say 'OK' when he has the answer.

If it took about the same amount of time for each, then the 5 is in the right hand since 1 x 17 is easy to compute. If the 2nd one was much slower, then the 5 is in the left hand.

The next time you do the trick, use different numbers like 13 or 19.

Write your answer (15) on a slip of paper, fold it, and lay it on the table.

Give your friend the paper and pencil.

Ask him to draw a Tic-Tac-Toe board.

Ask him to write down the numerals 1 to 9 in order in the diagram.
1, 2, 3 on top. 4, 5, 6 middle. 7, 8, 9 on bottom.

Have him circle any numeral in the first row.

Have him circle any numeral in the second row that is not in the same column as the first one circled.

Have him circle the numeral in the bottom row that is in the column with no circled numerals.

Tell him to add up the circled numbers.

Then ask him to unfold your answer – 15!

PREPARATION:

Put a red spot on one piece of paper, blue on another, green on the third.
On the back of the red paper, write in small neat printing – 'YOU CHOSE RED'.

On an envelope where the stamp would go, write
'YOU CHOSE BLUE' – not too big so you can cover it with your thumb.

On the fourth piece of paper, write 'YOU CHOSE GREEN', fold it,
and put it in the envelope.

Put the three marked papers in the envelope and now the trick is ready.

INSTRUCTIONS:

Pull the envelope out of your bag covering the writing with your
fingers and lay it front down on the table.
Slide the three colored papers out and lay them in a line on the
table with the colors facing up.

Ask a friend to think of one of the colors. Really concentrate on it.
Say Kalamazoo and then ask her to tell you the color she chose.

If she says 'BLUE' put the papers back into the envelope,
fold the flap over to close it and then hold up the front and have your
friend read what is written there.
If she says 'RED' turn over the Green, then Blue, then Red papers and
have her read what is written.
If she says 'GREEN', pick up the envelope and spread it open so she can
see the paper inside. Ask her to take it out and read what is on it as you pick
up the papers and put them away.
Immediately retrieve the materials and put them away before they can
be inspected. Do not do the same trick twice.

Bet your friend that he will not be able to jump over a coin when you set it down. Have him stand with his arms straight down at his sides and then place the coin on top of his head.

If he complains that you tricked him, then give him another chance – put the coin in the very corner of the room.

Ask someone to write a three-digit number whose digits decrease in value, e.g. 921.

Then ask them to write the same number backwards underneath it (129) and subtract the second number from the first (792).

Ask them what the last digit is.

Take the last digit away from 9 and this will give you the first digit of the answer.

The middle digit is **always 9**.

Cut out a strip of paper about 12in/30cm long and 1.5in/3cm wide. Draw a small cross at both ends of the strip on one side of the paper only. Twist the paper once and stick the ends together with tape with the crosses facing each other. The crosses will then be hidden. Cut along the center legthways and the loop starts to divide in two. But the further you cut, the loop becomes one double-sized loop.

Can you see what's wrong with this upside-down face.
Solution on page 96.

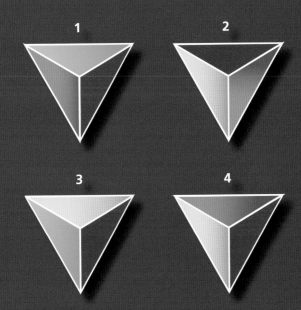

Look at the pyramids. A regular pyramid has four faces that are equilateral triangles and each one is painted either red, blue, green or yellow. The pyramid is rotated and these four different bird's-eye views are made by looking down on each of its four corners. Which one of these views is incorrect? Solution on page 96.

Page 12

Page 13
Take a piece of fruit from the barrel marked 'M'. As this is wrongly labeled it cannot contain both oranges and lemons. If, for example, it contains 'oranges' you know that 'L', which cannot contain lemons, must therefore contain the mixture of oranges and lemons, 'O' must contain lemons.

Page 17
Start by having the coins: head, head, tail. Then turn over 1 & 3, 1 & 2, then 1 & 3.

Page 18
C.

Page 20
F.

Page 21
No it cannot.

Page 22

AH	KS	QC	JD
QD	JC	AS	KH
JS	QH	KD	AC
KC	AD	JH	QS

Page 24
Take one match from the middle top row and the two matches which form the bottom right hand corner.

Page 26
B.

Page 32

Page 34

Page 35
They are the same.

Page 36
Only the first one.
The second one is impossible.

Page 38

Page 39
They're the same.

Page 40
64.

Page 43
1296.

Page 45

Page 46
C.

Page 48
Well done. The code is:

Page 50

Page 51
They are the same.

Page 52

Page 55
This is one solution.

Page 56

Page 57
They do not move.

Page 58
1024 ways.

Page 60

Page 65
105.

Page 69
No.

Page 71

Page 79

Page 81
D.

Page 82
The word 'DIOXIDE' is reversed too, but its symmetry enables you to read it.

Page 85
Pour the liquid in glass 2 into glass 7 and the liquid in glass 4 into glass 9.

Page 92
Her face is upside-down but the smile is the right way up.

Page 93
View 2. The views in 2 and 4 both have green as the base, therefore 1 and 3 must be correct. From view 3, looking at the top-right hand corner with green as the base, the correct colors are red, blue, yellow, which is the same as view 4, which means that view 2 is incorrect.